# Topsy Turvy
# CHRISTMAS

## A musical play for Christmas

# Lucy Moore

*For Oliver, Anna and Angus McKinney with much love*

*Many thanks to Angela Crunkhorn and to all the staff at Padnell Junior School for your patience and enthusiasm in the field-testing. To Paul and Neil for all your musical know-how.*

*And very special thanks to the Butterwick and Padnell children for your hard work and brilliant ideas that went into the production.*

Text copyright © Lucy Moore 2003
Illustrations copyright © Francis Blake 2003
Music copyright © Lucy and Paul Moore 2003
Musical arrangements copyright © Neil Ogley 2003

The author asserts the moral right
to be identified as the author of this work

**Published by**
**The Bible Reading Fellowship**
First Floor, Elsfield Hall
15–17 Elsfield Way, Oxford OX2 8FG
ISBN 1 84101 340 4

First published 2003
10 9 8 7 6 5 4 3 2 1 0
All rights reserved

A catalogue record for this book is available from the British Library

Printed and bound in Malta

# CONTENTS

Scene 1:     Topsy turvy chant; Topsy turvy world

Scene 2:     Nazareth calypso

Scene 3:     Heaven's just for us

Scene 4:     Joseph's song

Scene 5:     Moving on blues

Scene 6:     Innkeeper's song

Scene 7:     Shepherds' rap; Angels' song

Scene 8:     Star song; Treasure song

Scene 9:     Topsy turvy chant

Scene 10:    We're going to see the king!

Scene 11:    Meet the baby; Topsy turvy world *(reprise)*; Topsy turvy chant

# INTRODUCTION

*Topsy Turvy Christmas* shows the events of the first Christmas as seen by two angels who are skiving off choir practice to watch 'television'—or rather, what is happening on Planet Earth 2000 years ago. Why does Christmas seem topsy turvy? Because, from the angels' perspective, the events appear nonsensical. God's Son leaving heaven and going to earth? Ridiculous! His mother being a common-or-garden teenager, not even a princess? Absurd! Jesus born in a horrible, uncomfortable cowshed? Completely unsuitable! The angels become more and more distraught until eventually they are drawn into the story themselves and discover in the stable that God's plan is 'so upside down, it's the right way up'.

Peopled with a cast of colourful characters, from confident Mary to majestic Gabriel, from the shepherds with their rustic rap to the bossy innkeeper and her meek husband, *Topsy Turvy Christmas* is a hilarious, gentle, thought-provoking look at the beautiful Christmas story.

The songs range from the mysterious 'Treasure song' of the kings to the energetic rock 'n' roll of the angelic choir in the 'Angels' song', and can be performed with the CD as backing or with as many instruments playing live as you have available. The music notation for all the songs starts on page 34.

The more fun the children have practising and performing the play, the more the audience will enjoy it—some of the wackier ideas in the script have come from children themselves, and your children are bound to have brilliant ideas of their own as well.

The play was written for a primary school teacher who wanted a Christmas play that actually told the Christmas story and didn't put pixies and reindeer in the starring roles. I'm deeply grateful to the two schools who field-tested it under very different circumstances. Butterwick Primary School tackled it as a class project as part of an evening of carols and other Christmas songs, and had a cast of about 30 children from Year 5. The music was accompanied by a piano and a small band. Padnell Junior School performed it as their Christmas production for two year groups combined, involving 200 children from Years 3 and 4. They used recorded music as accompaniment.

The performance lasts between 50 and 60 minutes, depending on how many traditional carols are included alongside the songs written especially for the play.

Topsy Turvy

# CHRISTMAS

# DIRECTOR'S NOTES

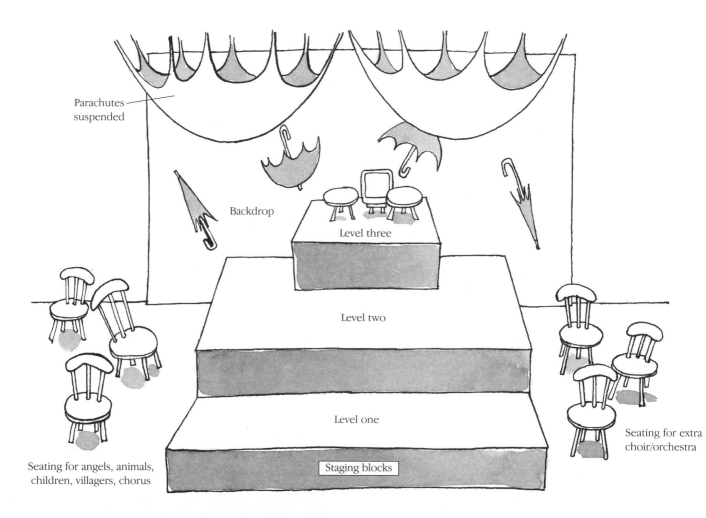

Parachutes suspended

Backdrop

Level three

Level two

Level one

Staging blocks

Seating for angels, animals, children, villagers, chorus

Seating for extra choir/orchestra

## ★ ★ STAGING, SET AND DECORATIONS ★ ★

The play is deliberately written to need as little scenery as possible. Any suggestions in the text are entirely optional and depend on the resources and space you have available.

Ideally, the stage would be on three levels, with a large area on the 'ground' level for the majority of the actors to use, a slightly raised second level and a small third level which Loreal and Ariel use as 'heaven'. However, you could simply put Loreal and Ariel on a separate piece of staging to one side. They will need a chair each.

As a backdrop, an abstract design of bright umbrellas (see above) in Christmassy colours, or patterns that pick up on the idea of upside down / topsy turvy, would be good. (You could perhaps use symmetrical patterns with contrasting colours, or patterns based on spirals / circles / spinning). If you are using the umbrella theme, umbrellas could be suspended from the ceiling. A parachute hung upside down makes a great enormous umbrella-like shape as a canopy for all or part of the stage, and adds colour.

You may want to put gym mats down on the stage for the gymnastics in Scene 1 and to deaden the sound of clomping feet.

If extended work is required, separate pictures to decorate the hall or classroom could be made, representing different scenes of the play. Each class could create one of the following:

★ Heaven: theme of angels, purity, richness
★ Nazareth: carpentry theme
★ Bethlehem: seen from far off
★ Bethlehem: theme of stable, animals
★ Shepherds: theme of crooks, sheep, night sky
★ Kings: theme of wealth, colour, the Orient
★ Final scene: theme of celebration, joy

## UMBRELLAS

A suggestion to create instant colour and movement is to use umbrellas as props wherever possible. Umbrellas can be up or down, making weird and wonderful shapes. Twirled or raised *en masse*, they create a marvellous effect if you want to keep scenery to a minimum. If you decide to use umbrellas, start asking everybody to bring one in, labelled clearly with name and class, at the start of the rehearsal period. That way, you may have enough for one each by the production date! A set of rainbow-coloured children's umbrellas could also be purchased for moments when you want a particularly bright and 'together' effect: they are only a couple of pounds each.

Explain the fragility of umbrellas, as well as the hazards of spikes and up-and-down mechanisms, and say that anyone who is silly will have their umbrella removed for good. Before starting rehearsals, play some games with umbrellas in order to:

★ use umbrellas safely and confidently
★ help children to think creatively about using umbrellas to suggest different objects
★ create mood with umbrellas
★ practise still pictures
★ practise performing (especially awareness of how the audience will see them)
★ work together in groups, listening to each other's suggestions
★ practise taking direction

### Suggested drama games / exercises using umbrellas

Put an umbrella in the middle of the circle, and say that it looks like an umbrella but isn't an umbrella any longer. Ask each person to walk into the circle and use the umbrella as anything except an umbrella. Everyone else has to guess what it is. (If the umbrella is open, it must not be closed and vice versa.)

Put some music on. Each person takes an umbrella, and all move round the room. Stop the music and call out an object. (Objects from the song 'Topsy turvy world' include a space rocket, cutlery, satellite dishes, pens, test-tubes, guns and missiles.) Children use the umbrellas to make that object. Freeze, praise their imagination, start the music and repeat with different objects to create.

Put the children in groups according to the colour of their umbrellas. Ask them to decide what word best fits the colour—'gloomy', 'excited', or 'peaceful'. They should make a 'sculpture' using their umbrellas and their bodies to depict this word.

Ask the children to use their umbrellas to express these verbs—*twirl, spin, turn, roll*—and to hold them still to express these adjectives—*upside down, confused, joyful, sad, energetic.*

★★★★★★★★★ **PROPS** ★★★★★★★★★

**You will need:**
Many umbrellas (if used)

**Scene 1:** large version of *Radio Times*
bowl and spoon
large remote control for TV

**Scene 2:** glitter / shiny paper confetti for Gabriel
ornate umbrella for Gabriel (if used)

**Scene 4:** Joseph's plan

**Scene 5:** suitcases / non-rustly carrier bags
inn sign (optional) (you could give it the same name as a local pub)
xylophone

**Scene 6:** expensive menu

**Scene 7:** plate of cakes
crooks and sticks (unless umbrellas are being used)
toy sheep

**Scene 8:** star on a stick
ornate umbrellas for kings (if used)
gifts
map

**Scene 10:** baby
manger (optional)
blankets

The stage directions given are only suggestions! For the scenes which have more complicated blockings, we've included diagrams here to show how they could work. You may wish to adapt these suggestions to fit your stage and suit your children, or you may well have different brilliant ideas about how to stage a scene. The choice is yours!

### Scene 1: Opening 'Topsy turvy chant'

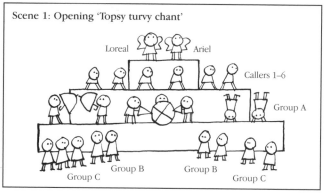

### Scene 1: 'Topsy turvy world' song

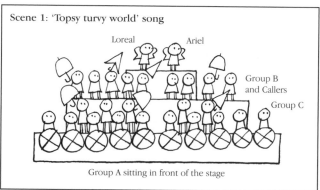

Group A sitting in front of the stage

### Scene 2

### Scene 4

### Scene 5

### Scene 7

### Scene 8

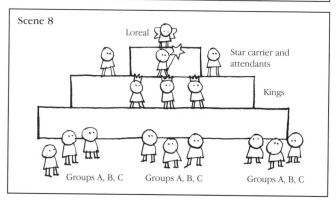

### Scene 10 (beginning)

### Scene 10 (end)

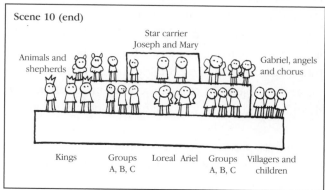

Modern costume is fun and relatively easy: you can get good vivid effects by dressing all the chorus parts in bright, plain T-shirts and jeans. Try the following for main cast characters:

★ Mary in trendy blue clothes
★ Joseph in workman's overalls
★ Gabriel in white (we happened to be able to lay hands on a small Royal Navy uniform, which looked great)
★ angels in white and yellow T-shirts (Loreal and Ariel could have fancier trimmings)
★ villagers with headscarves or hats and coats
★ shepherds in sloppy 'street' clothes—whatever is in fashion (for example, hooded tops and beanie hats)
★ sheep in white t-shirts with black masks
★ the kings either in lab coats or more traditional exotic Eastern garb
★ the Star Carrier and attendants in anything light and sparkly
★ the innkeeper and her husband in evening dress
★ the farmer in wellies and jeans
★ animals with masks
★ children in everyday coats

Plimsolls will keep that incredibly loud thumping noise of children's feet to a minimum.

Live music is definitely fun, and all the scores can be found at the end of the script, starting on page 34. If, however, live music isn't an option for you, the songs, both sung and with backing tracks only, can also be found on the *Topsy Turvy Christmas* CD, which is available as an accompaniment to this book.

If you do have the facilities for live music, a keyboard and small band would be ideal. If you don't have enough musicians, could you perhaps work with your local secondary school? A further suggestion would be to mix and match styles: use some live music and some recorded music from the CD.

You could have children adding a simple percussion accompaniment to the songs, or as sound effects (for example, in Scene 4 in the carpentry shop, or for the entrance of the star or angels).

You could add pop songs and dances if there is something Christmassy in the charts that is appropriate (for example, to give the farm animals a little longer on stage or to make more of the entrance of the angels, or to cover the entrances in Scene 10).

NB: Don't forget to contact PRS about performance rights if you're charging for tickets and using recorded music other than the *Topsy Turvy Christmas* CD.

## EXTRA CAROLS

In the script you will see suggestions for optional traditional carols. These are not integral to the plot, but could be included if you want a slightly longer performance and one in which the audience can be invited to participate. The words and scores are not included in this book as they are all readily available elsewhere. However, some traditional carols are included on the *Topsy Turvy Christmas* CD for your convenience.

## ★ ★ ★ ★ ★ ★ ★ ★ ★ CAST ★ ★ ★ ★ ★ ★ ★ ★ ★

The cast for *Topsy Turvy Christmas* is designed for the minimum of one average-sized class, and a cast of 30 people upwards would work well. The maximum number of performers will be dictated by the limit of your stage! In the cast list you will see which parts can be played by any of the children, and which parts require some degree of acting / line-learning skill. 'Umbrella carriers' are chorus-type parts.

The play can be performed with as few as 15 actors, but if you perform it with this number of people you will need to double up some of your characters and merge the minor parts (like callers, villagers and shepherds) into smaller numbers.

# THE CAST

NB: Parts marked * need reasonable acting / speaking skills. Parts marked ** need your best actors.

★ Six callers
★ Ariel**—an angel (the younger of the two, slightly nervous, not used to doing anything naughty. Male or female)
★ Loreal**—an angel (bossy, grumpy, bit of a rebel, lots of attitude. Male or female)
★ Gabriel* (has presence)
★ Mary* (vivacious)
★ Joseph* (solemn, with a good singing voice)
★ Town crier* (loud)
★ Martha*—Nazareth villager
★ Joshua*—Nazareth villager
★ Anna*—Nazareth villager
★ Jehu*—Nazareth villager
★ Jeremiah*—Nazareth villager
★ Innkeeper* (bouncy extrovert)
★ Innkeeper's husband* (henpecked)
★ Joe*—shepherd (streetwise, can rap)
★ Harry*—shepherd (streetwise, can rap)
★ Sam*—shepherd (streetwise, can rap)
★ Fred*—shepherd (streetwise, can rap)

★ Sid*—shepherd (streetwise and slightly dimmer than the others, but can rap. Comic timing needed)
★ Star carrier (needs to sing but doesn't otherwise speak)
★ Caspar* (has authority)
★ Melchior* (has authority)
★ Balthasar* (has authority)
★ Three optional servants for the kings
★ Farmer
★ Jemima—Bethlehem child
★ Hannah—Bethlehem child
★ Daniel—Bethlehem child
★ Simon—Bethlehem child
★ Any number of umbrella carriers in three groups— A, B and C
★ Any number of other shepherds
★ Any number of sheep (especially if they can do a simple step-dance to a rap)
★ Any number of angels (especially if they can rock-and-roll)
★ Any number of star attendants
★ Any number of servants for the three kings
★ Any number of farm animals
★ Any number of other Bethlehem children
★ Any number of singers
★ Any number of instrumentalists

# THE PLAY

★ ★ ★ ★ ★ ★ ★ ★ ★ ★ ★ ★ ★ ★ ★ ★ ★ ★ ★ ★ ★ ★ **★ ★ ★**     SCENE 1     **★ ★** ★ ★ ★ ★ ★ ★ ★ ★ ★ ★ ★ ★ ★ ★ ★ ★ ★ ★ ★ ★ ★

*Optional carol: Angels from the realms of glory*

The introduction to this scene is slightly surreal, but don't let that put you off. It gives the audience time to get used to the size of the cast and the voices without losing any of the plot. It also sets the theme clearly and is great fun to do. However, if the mere thought panics you, miss out the following actions and start straight in with the 'Topsy turvy chant'.

*Group A of the umbrella carriers walk on during the introductory music and freeze in position on level 1 of the stage.*

*The six callers walk on and stand on level 2 behind them.*

*Groups B and C of the umbrella carriers crouch in the aisles among the audience.* **NB: Mary and Joseph need to be among Group B.**

*As the music stops, a percussionist continues the beat. After four beats, groups B and C whisper on every other beat, 'Topsy turvy'. They keep this going. It should sound slightly spooky at first, and build in intensity. (It's a great exercise for listening skills and group work.)*

*Group A (on stage) stay frozen for the moment.*

*When everyone is in position, the callers start calling their words out on the alternate beats.*

| | |
|---|---|
| **Caller 1:** | Inside out! |
| **B and C:** | *(whispering)* Topsy turvy. |
| **Caller 2:** | Upside down! |
| **B and C:** | *(whispering)* Topsy turvy. |
| **Caller 3:** | Head over heels! |
| **B and C:** | *(whispering)* Topsy turvy. |
| **Caller 4:** | Back to front! |
| **B and C:** | *(whispering)* Topsy turvy. |
| Caller 5: | Round and round! |
| **B and C:** | *(whispering)* Topsy turvy. |
| **Caller 6:** | Wheels in wheels! |
| **B and C:** | *(whispering)* Topsy turvy. |
| **Caller 1:** | Inside out! |
| **B and C:** | *(shouting)* Inside out! |
| **Caller 2:** | Upside down! |
| **B and C:** | *(shouting)* Upside down! |
| **Caller 3:** | Head over heels! |
| **B and C:** | *(shouting)* Head over heels! |
| **Caller 4:** | Back to front! |
| **B and C:** | *shouting)* Back to front! |
| **Caller 5:** | Round and round! |
| **B and C:** | *(shouting)* Round and round! |
| **Caller 6:** | Wheels in wheels! |
| **B and C:** | *(shouting)* Wheels in wheels! |

*All sing 'Topsy turvy chant'.*

*As the chant starts, groups B and C stand in the aisles and twirl their umbrellas on the spot.*

*Group A come to life and move in ways suggested by the words—stylized spins, rolls, cartwheels, somersaults, depending on how gymnastic they can be, some using their umbrellas (furled and unfurled, spinning, turning them, jumping over them and so on). The impression should be one of colour, movement and organized chaos. They end the chant frozen, holding the umbrellas to make an interesting group shape.*

---

## Topsy turvy chant

Inside out and upside down
and all head-over-heels are turning
Back to front and round and round
and wheels in wheels in wheels are turning
Bottoms up and wrong side out
and willy-nilly vice versa
Crazy, madcap, Christmas crackers,
tables turned and hurdy-gurdy,
Topsy turvy Christmas time!

---

*Group A sit in front of the stage with their umbrellas open and pointed towards audience to make a colourful front. **Group B** take up position on the stage on level 2. The callers can now join group B. **Group C** take up position on the stage on level 1. They all freeze.*

*All sing 'Topsy turvy world'. During the song, groups B and C make moving tableaux of the suffering being described. They now use their umbrellas as props to emphasize the words.*

*In verse 1, on level 1, enemy soldiers crouch with guns in trenches facing each other. Meanwhile, on level 2, umbrellas are held horizontally above the children's heads like missiles, and they slowly 'fly' them across the stage.*

*In verse 2, the children on level 1 become children with open umbrellas as begging bowls. On level 2, the children use their umbrellas (closed) as knives and forks, or (open) as bowls of food, or simply*

*rub their stomachs greedily. One 'posh' couple with closed umbrellas over their arms walk through the beggars, flicking them away in disgust.*

*In verse 3, on level 1, umbrellas are used to show a rocket being launched upwards, while others are used as pens and test-tubes for learned scientists. On level 2, they are opened out and held wrong-side-up to be like satellite dishes panning the skies, slowly moving from left to right and back again.*

✦✦✦✦✦✦✦✦✦✦✦✦✦✦✦✦✦✦✦✦✦✦✦✦✦✦✦

## Topsy turvy world

It's a topsy turvy world we live in
We long for peace but we end up with war
It's a topsy turvy world we live in
We have enough and we still long for more
And we fight and we kill
for a few miles of ground
It's a topsy turvy world we live in
Find me a place where it all comes
right way round.

It's a topsy turvy world we live in
Children go hungry and starve on the street
It's a topsy turvy world we live in
Others are dying from too much to eat
And there's plenty for all
if we shared it around
It's a topsy turvy world we live in
Find me a time when it all comes
right way round

It's a topsy turvy world we live in
We fly into space but so many don't know
In this topsy turvy world we live in
About him who made us to live,
love and grow
And we've found out so much,
but there's one we've not found.
It's a topsy turvy world we live in
Find me the one who will bring the
right way round.

✦✦✦✦✦✦✦✦✦✦✦✦✦✦✦✦✦✦✦✦✦✦✦✦✦✦✦

*Groups B and C sit on level 2.*

*Two angels, Loreal and Ariel, tiptoe in from opposite directions, looking all around them, bump into each other from behind and jump. It is obvious that they should not be there and have a guilty conscience about it.*

**Ariel:** Oh dear, Loreal. We really ought to be at band practice!

**Loreal:** Don't get your halo in a twist, Ariel! I'm fed up with band practice.

**Ariel:** Yes so am I. But what if someone finds us here in the TV room?

**Loreal:** No one will find us here! And look! (*Shows Ariel the* Radio Times) There are some really good things to see on the terrestrial channel tonight.

**Ariel:** The terrestrial channel?

**Loreal:** On Planet Earth!

**Ariel:** (*Starts to leave*) But the band! They'll miss me and my trumpet!

**Loreal:** (*Pulls her back*) Look! It says Gabriel's starring!

**Ariel:** Gabriel? Down on Planet Earth? Wow! Are you sure?

**Loreal:** Yeah! You don't see Big Gabe on Earth very often, now, do you?

**Ariel:** Ooooh... I wonder what's going on. Perhaps I'll just watch TV for a little while, then.

**Loreal:** Here, have a bowl of this while I switch on the big screen.

**Ariel:** What is it?

**Loreal:** Angel Delight. (*He points a remote control towards the stage area*) Just in time—there's Gabriel!

**Ariel:** Turn up the volume!

*Optional carol: It came upon the midnight clear*

*Gabriel walks through the audience. His huge umbrella is white and lavishly decorated with tinsel and glitter. As he goes through the audience, he scatters scraps of glittery paper or throws glitter around him.*

*All sing with appropriate swaying and Hawaiian dancer-type arm movements.*

★★★★★★★★★★★★★★★★★★★★★★★★★★★★

## Nazareth calypso

There's an angel walkin' into town tonight
In our dirty streets he's a radiant light
And his wings brush the shabby houses,
making them bright.
Oh oh! This angel is a marvellous sight.
Oh yes! This angel is a marvellous sight.

★★★★★★★★★★★★★★★★★★★★★★★★★★★★

**Gabriel:**  *(During musical lull between verses, still in the aisle)* Nazareth. So this is the place. Now where is the girl?

*Mary moves on to level 1, happily engrossed in dancing with her umbrella.*

★★★★★★★★★★★★★★★★★★★★★★★★★★★★

**Verse 2**
There's a young girl singin' to her God tonight
A joyful song 'cos she's full of light.
She's about to get herself a terrible fright.
Oh oh! About to see a marvellous sight.
Oh yes! About to see a marvellous sight.

★★★★★★★★★★★★★★★★★★★★★★★★★★★★

*The umbrella carriers settle down as background on level 2. Gabriel arrives on level 1 and passes his umbrella to a member of group B.*

Gabriel: Greetings, Mary.

*Mary doesn't hear and carries on dancing happily.*

Gabriel: Greetings, Mary… Oh, this is
ridiculous.

*He taps her on the shoulder. She jumps in shocked surprise, and drops the umbrella.*

Gabriel: Hello Mary. *(He can't help beaming
with delight—it's as if he's going to tell
her she's won the jackpot in the
Lottery)* You are blessed from head to
toe. The Lord is with you.

Mary: What's happening? Who are you? What
do you mean?

Gabriel: Don't be scared! *(He kneels down in
front of her)*

Mary: But you're an angel!

Gabriel: God is pleased with you…

Mary: With me?

Gabriel: …and you will have a son…

Mary: But…

Gabriel: His name will be Jesus. He will be great
and will be called Son of the Most High.

Mary: I…

Gabriel: He will rule the people of Israel for
ever, and his kingdom will never end.

Mary: How can this possibly happen? I'm not
even married!

Gabriel: The Holy Spirit will come down to
you.

Mary: *(By now totally gobsmacked. She
opens her arms in a gesture of
'Fantastic! Great!)* I am God's servant.
Let's go for it! I must tell Joseph…

Gabriel: *(To audience)* This is going to be fun!

*Mary runs into Group B. Gabriel gets his umbrella and moves off through the audience. All sing.*

---

**Verse 3**

There's a Spirit moving in the house tonight,
Mary reckons it'll be all right.
Goes along with God without a fight.
Oh oh! She wants to help him put things right.
Oh yes! She wants to help him put things right.

---

*Ariel and Loreal are staring at the stage in disbelief.*

**Loreal:** Gabriel knelt down! An archangel knelt down in front of a teenager! I don't believe it!

**Ariel:** Not just that—did you hear what he said to her? She's going to have God's baby! A common little working-class girl like that, and she thinks she's going to be mother to the Son of God?

**Loreal:** Oh Ariel, I don't like it—the world is turning upside down. The old rules don't seem to apply any more.

*Loreal and Ariel sing this song with the angel chorus joining in on the choruses.*

## Heaven's just for us

**Chorus**

*Hang on a minute—what is going on?*
*Hang on a minute—it's all going wrong!*
*Hang on a minute—we won't make a fuss*
*But all of this belongs in heaven*
*and heaven's just for us!*

**Verse 1**

Now God could take the wealth of heaven
And drop it on the earth.
These piles of gold, these precious jewels
This very air is worth a fortune.
All these riches, all this beauty—
it's so glorious
But all of this belongs in heaven
And heaven's just for us!

**Chorus…**

**Verse 2**

And God could take the love of heaven
And pour it on the planet.
Love that changes lives around
That softens granite hearts and minds.
Oh, all this tender Father's love—
there's plenty of surplus
But all of this belongs in heaven
And heaven's just for us!

**Chorus…**

**Verse 3**

And God could take the joy of heaven
And wrap it round the world
Like a lovely rainbow ribbon
Every inch all curled and dancing.
All this laughter, all this fun—it's so obvious
That all of this belongs in heaven
And heaven's just for us!

**Chorus…**

| | |
|---|---|
| **Ariel:** | Yes, it's all very odd. Change channel or something! |
| **Loreal:** | Good idea. Oh look, there's a DIY programme on this channel. Let's try that. |
| **Ariel:** | DIY? What does that mean? Doughnuts In Yoghurt? |
| **Loreal:** | No, you noodle—Do It Yourself. How to build your own halo stand, you know the sort of thing. |
| **Ariel:** | That sounds fun. |

*Loreal points the remote control at the stage area. Groups B and C become carpenters. They mime / use umbrellas like saws, axes, screwdrivers, hammers, planes.*

*Make percussion noises of hammering, sawing, scraping and so on.*

*Joseph is in front of them all on level 1, studying his plan.*

*Mary comes in to Joseph on level 1.*

**Mary:** Joseph!

*Carpenters carry on carpenting. Mary tries shouting louder.*

**Mary:** Joseph!

*He still doesn't hear. Mary bellows.*

**Mary:** Joseph! I'm going to have God's baby!

*All stop, fall silent and gasp*

**Joseph:** But, Mary, you're supposed to be marrying me!
**Mary:** I still want to marry you, Joseph.
**Jospeh:** But… But … This is a bit of a shock, dear.
**Mary:** It is to me as well, love.
**Joseph:** Look—just let me think this through, would you?

*Mary goes and sits to one side of the stage while Joseph sings 'Joseph's song'. All join in the choruses.*

*In the choruses, Joseph is studying his plan.*

*In verse 1, Joseph walks about thinking.*

*In verse 2, he mimes asking the carpenters what he should do. They shake their heads and look doubtfully at Mary.*

*In verse 3, sung by Gabriel, Gabriel comes and stands by him. Joseph gives him the plan and goes to hold Mary's hands (if he can bear the embarrassment).*

---

✦ ✦ ✦ ✦ ✦ ✦ ✦ ✦ ✦ ✦ ✦ ✦ ✦ ✦ ✦ ✦ ✦ ✦ ✦ ✦ ✦ ✦ ✦ ✦ ✦

## Joseph's Song

**Verse 1**
All I ever wanted was a peaceful life
The safety of my job and then a faithful wife
A stable happy home and a normal family
Now it seems the strangest things are
happening to me.

**Chorus**
*Joseph, you had your life planned out*
*Joseph, in your quiet little town*
*Joseph, you'd ruled surprises out*
*But God's about to turn your plans*
*upside down.*

**Verse 2**
All I ever wanted was a son to teach
About the wood and nails and the price of each
And all I asked from life was predictability
Now it seems the strangest things are
happening to me.

**Chorus…**

**Verse 3**
All you ever wanted was to do God's will
Deep inside your heart you know you
want that still
Take Mary as your wife—the baby's God's,
it's true
You will love the strange things that are
happening to you.

**Chorus…**

★ ★ ★ ★ ★ ★ ★ ★ ★ ★ ★ ★ ★ ★ ★ ★ ★ ★ ★ ★ ★ ★ ★ ★ ★

Reproduced with permission from *Topsy Turvy Christmas* published by BRF 2003 (1 84101 340 4)

**Loreal:** But that's Gabriel! I mean Gabriel!

**Ariel:** The celestial Big Cheese!

**Loreal:** And he's talking to a workman! What's heaven coming to?

**Ariel:** *(Fiddling with the remote control)* Heaven's coming down to earth, by the look of it.

*Optional carol: Thou who wast rich beyond all splendour*

**Loreal:** *(Shaking head)* Heaven on earth? I don't know—standards are slipping… Heaven just isn't what it used to be.

**Ariel:** Nor is earth, by the look of it. Loreal? What happens if you press this button?

*Groups B and C join group A on level 1. They are all now the villagers of Nazareth. Mary and Joseph come out last of all. Mary is now heavily pregnant, and Joseph carries both their suitcases.*

**Loreal:** Look out—you've pressed the fast forward button! We must have skipped a few months. What are the villagers doing now?

**Town crier:** *(To fx of irritating airport ding-dong on xylophone)* Good morning, Nazareth travellers! All those leaving for the census trip to Bethlehem, please join the party at the village gate! The census trip to Bethlehem is about to leave! All those born in Bethlehem, please proceed to gate 2! This is your final call for the Bethlehem departure! *(Repeat fx)*

*The named villagers and Mary and Joseph stand on level 2. They are very cheesed off.*

**Martha:** Oh dear! It's such a long way to Bethlehem.

**Joshua:** Leaving behind everything we know.

**Anna:** The wretched Romans!

**Jehu:** Turning our lives upside down!

**Jeremiah:** And all for their flipping census.

**All:** It's senseless.

**Martha:** Who's going to water my pot plants?

**Joshua:** Who's going to feed the cat?

**Anna:** I hate long journeys—they're so BORING.

**Jehu:** I always get travelsick on a donkey.

**Jeremiah:** Yes, and there's always so much traffic on the roads at Christmas time.

*Sing through 'Moving on blues' twice. Groups A, B and C use opened umbrellas as car wheels and steering wheels to create the illusion of a traffic jam. All click fingers rhythmically.*

*On the second time through the song, all the villagers—except the named ones and Mary and Joseph—leave and trudge off stage. The named villagers and Mary and Joseph carry on walking across the stage wearily.*

## Moving on blues

I've got those moving on blues.
(Da da da da da da da da da da)
'Cos I had to leave my home
(Da da da da da da da da da da)
Though there's holes in my shoes
(Da da da da da da da da da da)
Me and my donkey, got to roam.
(Da da da da da da da da da da)

Leaving all my folk behind
(Da da da da da da da da da da)
Face an unknown world ahead
(Da da da da da da da da da da)
There are times this world ain't kind
(Da da da da da da da da da da)
Wish I could stay at home in bed
(Da da da da da da da da da da)

Oh how slow the miles pass
(Da da da da da da da da da da)
When the traffic's all in queues
(Da da da da da da da da da da)
Now my donkey's out of gas
(Da da da da da da da da da da)
I really got those moving on blues.
(Da da da da da da da da da da)

Ah-ha.

**Martha:** Are we nearly there yet?
**Joshua:** How many more miles?
**Anna:** I'm bored.
**Jeremiah:** I want to go home.
**Jehu:** Stop the donkey! I'm going to be sick.
**All:** Here we are—Bethlehem at last! Hooray!

*Optional carol: In the bleak midwinter*

*The named villagers wave goodbye to each other and walk off stage. Mary and Joseph look around and call.*

**Mary and Joseph:** Hello? Is there anyone there?

Reproduced with permission from *Topsy Turvy Christmas* published by BRF 2003 (1 84101 340 4)

## Innkeeper's song

We've plenty of room, come in, come in!
You're welcome, you're welcome to stay.
Our six-star hotel will ring out the bells
You're welcome, you're welcome today!

Roll out the red carpet and bow to the ground.
Let trumpeters fanfare—hooray!
You're our VIPs, oh, do sit down, please
You're welcome, you're welcome today!

We'll carry your luggage, we'll garage your ass.
Would you care for a small canapé?
You're special to us, you are worth all this fuss.
You're welcome, you're welcome today!

Oh, have some champagne! Take some
more caviar!
Of course we'll expect you to pay
But relax for the mo, 'cos we're longing
to show you
You're welcome, so welcome today!

*The innkeeper and her husband leap out to meet the travellers. He is carrying a posh menu.*

**Both:** *(Expansively)* Welcome! Welcome to Bethlehem!

**Joseph:** Have you got a room for the night?

**Husband:** Hmmm. Well, we're really quite full, what with the census and Bethlehem United playing at home…

**Joseph:** Look, my wife's about to have a baby!

**Innkeeper:** *(Shoves husband to one side and he falls flat on the floor)* Oh goody! I love babies! In that case, what would you say to a luxury four-poster bed in our honeymoon suite with private bathroom, sauna and jacuzzi and cooked full English breakfast in bed?

**Mary:** Fantastic! That's just the place for God's son to be born!

*Innkeeper and husband sing verses of 'Innkeeper's song'. All join in choruses.*

**Innkeeper:** Splendid! Well, you go and have a drink, and I'll make sure there are some clean towels out. Humphrey! Did you put a basket of fresh fruit in number 16?

**Husband:** Yes, dear.

**Innkeeper:** Champagne?

**Husband:** Yes, dear.

**Innkeeper:** Chocolates?

**Husband:** Yes, dear.

**Innkeeper:** Have you pleated the toilet paper?

**Husband:** What do you think this is—the *[local posh hotel]*?

*They usher Mary and Joseph offstage.*

**Ariel:** That's all going smoothly now, anyway. God's son can be born in the best hotel in Bethlehem in the lap of luxury.

**Loreal:** Yes. Much more suitable than that horrible little village. We can relax again.

**Ariel:** I wonder what the band's practising now? In fact, I wonder what *we* were practising for?

**Loreal:** Oh, forget about them. Have a slice of this.

**Ariel:** What is it?

**Loreal:** Angel cake. Now let's try a different channel. Ah, here we go. Ooh, nice night sky…

**Ariel:** Any sign of Patrick Moore? I like him.

**Loreal:** Nah—listen to those sheep. Must be a nature documentary.

*Enter five shepherds, using their umbrellas upside down as crooks, and making a fire of umbrellas like sticks. A flock of sheep also enter.*

*Optional carol: The first nowell or While shepherds watched*

## Shepherds' rap

*The heavy beat comes on the syllables in bold. The sheep provide the 'backing track' between lines. The shepherds line up for the rap. The sheep dance.*

**Joe:** I've **got** all I **want** on this **bare** hill**side**

**Sheep:** Baa baa a-baa baa baa

**Sam:** My **pipe** and my **fire** and my **crook** by my **side**

**Sheep:** Baa baa a-baa baa baa

**Fred:** I **go** to **sleep** as **much** as I **can**

**Sheep:** Baa baa a-baa baa baa

**Sid:** It's a **lovely life** for a **lazy man**.

**Sheep:** Baa baa a-baa baa baa

**Harry:** I **won't** pull the **wool over** your **eyes**es

**Sheep:** Baa baa a-baa baa baa

**Sam:** I **like** my **life** with **no** sur**prises**

**Sheep:** Baa baa a-baa baa baa

**Fred:** The **peaceful sound** of the **rustic bleat**

**Sheep:** Baa baa a-baa baa baa

**Sid:** And **plenty** of **nice** lamb **chops** to **eat**

**Sheep:** *(Indignantly)* Baa?

*Sheep graze. Shepherds sigh contentedly round the fire.*

**Joe:** Ah, 'tis good to be a shepherd.

**Harry:** You know where you are when you're a shepherd.

**Sam:** Aye. Sheep is sheep. Wool and mutton on legs.

**Fred:** You watch 'em graze.

**Sid:** Then you move 'em on.

**Joe:** Then you watch 'em graze.

| | |
|---|---|
| Harry: | Then you move 'em on. |
| Sam: | Then you dip 'em. |
| Fred: | Then you shear 'em. |
| Sid: | Then you watch 'em graze. |
| All: | And you move 'em on. |
| Joe: | Aye, you know where you are when you're a… |
| All: | What on earth is that????? |

*Gabriel appears behind them. Shepherds and sheep all fall on to their knees and put their heads down on the ground.*

| | |
|---|---|
| Gabriel: | Don't be afraid! I've got some good news for you, to make everyone happy. Today, in Bethlehem, a very special baby was born for you. You'll find him wrapped up and lying in a manger. |

*Optional carol: Hark, the herald angels sing*

*The shepherds do a short dumbshow of knees knocking, chewing knuckles, praying, and clutching sheep in terror to cover the entrance on to*

*level 2 of the angel choir, all with glittery white umbrellas. When they are in place, the shepherds speak.*

| | |
|---|---|
| Harry: | Oh dear, oh me, oh my. |
| Sam: | It shouldn't happen to a shepherd. |
| Fred: | I must be dreaming. |
| Sid: | I said we shouldn't have touched that sheep dip. |
| Ariel: | Look, Loreal! Look! It's the angels' band! They're in the sky above those shepherds! This is what we were practising for! Come on! We've just got time to join them! |
| Loreal: | Go down to earth? To that dump? When I could stay happily in heaven? Urgh. No thank you! |
| Ariel: | Oh come on! We can sneak into the back row! |
| Loreal: | My contract doesn't say anything about sharing my musical talents with a bunch of scruffy shepherds. |
| Ariel: | What? |
| Loreal: | If I'd known we were only practising for shepherds, I'd never have joined the band in the first place! |
| Ariel: | Well, I don't care what you say. I think this is an amazing occasion, and I'm going to be part of it! |

*Ariel grabs her umbrella and jumps down to join the back row of the choir.*

| | |
|---|---|
| Loreal: | Angels belong safe and sound in heaven, not on earth! Oh dear, oh dear. Everything's getting all mixed up. Topsy turvy. Upside down. What's the world coming to? |

*All sing the 'Angels' song', using rock-and-roll hand movements as described overleaf.*

| | |
|---|---|
| Ariel: | Wait for me! I'm here! |
| Gabriel: | OK! Hit the rhythm, angels! |

# Angels' song

**Chorus** *(x 2)*:
***From the highest of the high***
*(Point upwards with index fingers to the beat)*
***To the lowest of the low***
*(Point downwards likewise)*
***Let peace and love and blessings flow.***
*(Roll hands. On 'flow', spread arms out,*
*palms up)*

**Verse 1**
Higher than the highest thought
*(Raise arms up on each line)*
Higher than the starry sky
Higher price than any gift you've bought
He is God, the king on high.

**Chorus…**

**Verse 2**
To the ones the world ignored
*(Bring arms down on each line)*
To the outcasts and the poor
To the ones who try to please the Lord
God's peace comes for evermore.

**Chorus…**

**Verse 3**
So from the highest heights of glory *(Arms up)*
God has come to lowest earth. *(Arms down)*
Tell the world the Christmas story *(Arms out)*
Tell the world of Jesus' birth. *(Arms out)*

**Chorus…**

*Finish with arms out like chorus line.*

*The angels leave. The shepherds and sheep stand up.*

| | |
|---|---|
| **Joe:** | So what do we do now? |
| **Harry:** | We go to Bethlehem and find this baby, of course! |
| **Sam:** | What? We leave our sheep behind? |
| **Fred:** | Well… |
| **Sheep:** | Baaaa! |
| **Fred:** | They want to come too! |
| **Sid:** | Come on, then! Hurry up! |
| **All:** | Let's get to Bethlehem! |

*The shepherds run off. The sheep follow.*

Reproduced with permission from *Topsy Turvy Christmas* published by BRF 2003 (1 84101 340 4)

**Loreal:** Dear, dear, dear. How undignified! It's all beyond me. Let's see if there's something more highbrow on the other side…

*Optional carol: We three kings*

*Loreal changes channel. The star carrier and attendants enter through audience. They walk up on to level 2. Following them come groups A, B and C and the named villagers, who all sit in the aisles. The star carrier sings solo in the verses of 'Star song', with all the children joining in the chorus:*

## Star song

**Verse 1**
Back a billion years ago
God made me to twinkle so
Pouring light out into space
Shining for a time and place
Where new worlds and hopes begin
Where they'll see the newborn king.

**Chorus**
*Wisdom made me so bright*
*Shining out through the centuries*
*Wise scribes wrote of my meaning*
*While my rays of light were beaming*
*Wise men followed my light*
*If you're wise you'll follow me still.*

**Verse 2**
Back a thousand years ago
God wanted his friends to know
That his Son would come to them
And be born in Bethlehem
And they wrote in holy scrolls
Prophecies of what he told.

**Chorus…**

**Sing Chorus and Verse 3 together (unaccompanied):**

**Verse 3**
So I shine with all my might
Knowing that tonight's the night
When the plans of countless years
Come to all their fullness here.
His amazing perfect plan:
God has come to earth as man.

Reproduced with permission from *Topsy Turvy Christmas* published by BRF 2003 (1 84101 340 4)

*The star carrier and attendants stay on level 2. Caspar, Melchior and Balthasar walk on to level 1, peering at a map. They could have very ornate umbrellas carried by servants.*

**Loreal:** Oh good. Must be BBC4. A bit of culture. Now these look like more my sort of people! Nicely dressed… intelligent… educated… rich… They're not the sort to let their lives be turned upside down by a peasant baby in a country pub. Let's turn the volume up.

**Caspar:** *(Pointing into the distance)* Bethlehem! There it is!

**Melchior:** Funny that we should follow the star for three years only to come to… Bethlehem.

**Balthasar:** Yes, it's not very big, is it?

**Melchior:** Or very important.

**Balthasar:** Or very clean.

**Caspar:** King Herod's wise men told us the new king would be born in Bethlehem. It must be the place.

**Melchior:** Yes, but look. Think about what we left behind us back at home. The royal palaces… the state-of-the-art laboratories…

**Balthasar:** The jewels… the banquets… the beautiful robes…

**Melchior:** The great cities… the libraries… the universities…

**All:** Hot baths. *(They sigh in unison)*

**Melchior:** And we come to this grubby little town in the back of beyond.

**Caspar:** We saw his star in the east! We saw the star that told us the new king was born! We knew then that it was worth giving up all that luxury to follow the star. Why should you change your minds now?

**Balthasar:** Because how can the king of kings be born in such a shabby little town?

**Caspar:** For all I care, he could be born in a cow-shed! If you buy a priceless jewel, what does it matter if its box is made of rough wood?

**Melchior:** You're right, Caspar. Come on, let's go and find this king and worship him, wherever he is.

*As the 'Treasure song' is sung (twice), the three wise men and the rest of the cast do the hand movements as described below. The star and attendants move down and into the aisle towards the end of the first time through the song.*

## Treasure song

You're after hidden treasure
*(Hand shielding eyes, searching)*
You're after more than gold
The casket's rough and unrefined
*(Trace box in the air)*
But look inside and you will find
Riches untold. *(Arms in air)*

You're searching for a treasure
*(Searching again)*
Of far more worth than spice
Unlike the jar of frankincense *(Sniff wrists)*
Its fragrance mystic and intense
This has no price. *(Arms up)*

You're hunting for a treasure *(Searching)*
And there is only one
*(Point one finger into audience)*
That's worth more than the myrrh you bring
Far greater than the greatest king
*(Trace big circle with arms)*
God's own Son. *(Arms up)*

**Balthasar:** The star! There it is! Let's follow it to Bethlehem!

*As the song is sung a second time through, the three wise men point to the star and follow it around the stage and into the aisle to sit behind it. The star continues round the aisles and back up on to level 2 in the centre.*

Reproduced with permission from *Topsy Turvy Christmas* published by BRF 2003 (1 84101 340 4)

*On level 3, Ariel runs in and pulls Loreal up.*

**Ariel:** Quick Loreal! Quick! You've got to come! Something terrible's happened!

**Loreal:** What can be more terrible than all this ghastly upheaval that's already happened?

**Ariel:** They've run out of room in the inn!

**Loreal:** But Mary and Joseph had a posh room all ready to stay in!

**Ariel:** The innkeeper had already given the room to a double-glazing salesman!

**Loreal:** But…

**Ariel:** Mary and Joseph have nowhere to spend the night! And the baby's on its way! It's all going wrong! Do something!

**Loreal:** What do you expect me to do?

**Ariel:** Just come to Bethlehem quickly! Please, Loreal!

*Optional carol: Away in a manger or Silent night*

*Ariel drags a protesting Loreal down to level 1 as all chant the 'Topsy turvy chant'. Until s/he gets to the stable, Loreal sways around as though on a cakewalk or on a ship in a stormy sea—s/he is completely wobbly.*

## Topsy turvy chant

Inside out and upside down
and all head-over-heels are turning
Back to front and round and round
and wheels in wheels in wheels are turning
Bottoms up and wrong side out
and willy-nilly vice versa
Crazy, madcap, Christmas crackers,
tables turned and hurdy-gurdy,
Topsy turvy Christmas time!

*A procession of animals on level 1 stops the two angels crossing the stage. They stand in front of the stage.*

**Ariel:** *(Pointing to level 2)* The inn where I left Mary and Joseph is over there!

**Loreal:** Ugh! Planet Earth is so different from heaven. I feel most out of place. Look at me! I can hardly stand up straight!

**Ariel:** What are you doing with all those animals?

**Farmer:** I be putting them in the barn for the night.

**Loreal:** Nasty smelly things.

*Affronted baas and moos and so on as animals make their way on to level 2. Mary and Joseph join them on level 2 in front of the star. As the whole cast will shortly be joining them on stage, if you have room, Joseph can carry on the manger with the baby in it. If there isn't enough room, Mary can simply hold the baby.*

**Ariel:** Oh dear. Where can Mary and Joseph be?

**Loreal:** Ariel, please let me go home! This whole planet is so different from heaven, I feel homesick. My legs are all wobbly!

*The shepherds run in on level 1.*

**Farmer:** Oooh. More sheep. Plenty of room in 'ere.

**Joe:** This is the place!

**Harry:** Yeah! God's Son will be in here, mark my words.

**Sam and Fred:** Are you sure?

**Sid:** Yeah! Follow the sheep.

*The shepherds and sheep follow the animals on to level 2.*

**Ariel:** Why are they looking for God's Son in a cow-shed?

**Loreal:** It's all madness! Oh my knees!

*Gabriel and the angel chorus arrive on level 1.*

**Gabriel:** He's here! God's Son is here!

**Angels:** In a cow-shed?

**Gabriel:** Yes! Isn't it perfect?

*Gabriel and the angel chorus go up to level 2. The kings arrive on level 1.*

**Caspar:** Look! The star's come to rest over this cow-shed!

**Melchoir:** A cow-shed?

**Balthasar:** A cow-shed!

**Caspar:** Presents ready, everyone? Come on then—let's go in.

*The kings go to the side of level 1. A group of children enter on the other side of level 1.*

**Jemima:** *(Pointing to the star overhead)* This is the place where Jesus is.

**Daniel:** Can we go in?

**Hannah:** I don't know. Are children allowed, do you think?

**Simon:** Jesus isn't just for grown-ups, is he? Come on, let's go and see him.

**Martha:** Come on, everybody! Let's find the baby!

*The children stay on level 1, on the opposite side from the kings. All sing the appropriate verses and choruses of 'We're going to see the king!' (opposite)*

✥

*Groups A, B and C arrive on level 1 between the kings and the children. The villagers join the children. The innkeeper and her husband bustle on with armfuls of blankets, bump into each other and fall down.*

**Ariel:** What's going on?

**Innkeeper:** That poor young couple! I had to tell them all the rooms were taken.

**Husband:** And Joseph was so desperate, he said they'd sleep in the stable!

**Innkeeper:** And poor Mary was about to have the baby!

**Husband:** Oh dear! Oh dear! I must take them these blankets! Excuse me!

**Innkeeper:** Oh dear! Oh dear!

**Loreal:** Oh dear, oh dear, oh dear. This is simply not good enough. A stable!

**Ariel:** What are we waiting for? *(Loreal starts to walk away. Ariel pulls him back)* Where are you going?

**Loreal:** I'm an angel! I'm not going into a cow-shed!

**Ariel:** Oh yes you are!

**Loreal:** Oh no I'm not!

**Ariel:** Oh yes you…

**Loreal:** *(Trying to leave)* Look! I'll get my wings dirty. I'm heavensick.

**Ariel:** The shepherds have gone in…

**Loreal:** Well, they're only shepherds.

**Ariel:** The children went in!

**Loreal:** Well, they're only children.

**Ariel:** The three kings have gone in…

**Loreal:** Well, I'm an angel!

**Ariel:** God Almighty himself has chosen to be born in a stable and you think you're too important to go in?

**Loreal:** Oh! I feel wobbly enough not being in heaven—I'll feel completely out of place in a stable! My halo'll get bent! I'll lose my harp! I'll get cowpat on my…

**Ariel:** *(Interrupting)* Come on!

*Optional carol: See him lying on a bed of straw or O come, all ye faithful*

# We're going to see the king!

## Chorus

*We're so excited!* (Oh yes!)
*We're going to see the king*
*Everyone's invited!* (Oh yes!)
*We're all going in.*
*Don't care if we're rich or poor,*
*doesn't matter any more.*
*What matters is we're here for sure!*
(Oh yes!) *We're going to see the king!*

## Children

We know it's past our bedtime,
but we can't sleep a wink.
It feels more like playtime,
and we'd all like to think
That we can be with Jesus
any time of day or night
And so we've come to sit with him,
to cuddle him, chill out with him
We can't wait to be with him—
we're going to see the king!

Chorus…

## Kings

We know we're very tired
after our three-year trip
We ought to go to bed now
but we don't want to kip
We've come this far behind the star,
and now I think we're here!
And so we've come to speak to him,
to kneel to him, bow down to him
We can't wait to be with him—
we're going to see the king!

Chorus…

## Angels

We ought to be in paradise
but can't resist the urge
To see him with our own two eyes,
to fly right down to earth.
Our mighty God become a child?
Amazing, but it's true!
And so we've come to honour him,
to gaze on him and worship him.
We can't wait to be with him—
we're going to see the king!

Chorus…

## Shepherds / Farmer

We know we should be guarding
our sheep out on the hill
But it would be too hard when
we're so excited still.
We know we're only working-class,
the lowest of the low
But we've come to smile at him,
to sing to him, to play to him
We can't wait to be with him—
we're going to see the king!

Chorus…

## Animals

We know we're unhygienic
and we make a nasty smell
But we make the place look scenic
and we warm it up as well
We know we're only animals,
but God's our Maker too
And so we've come to stare at him,
to breathe on him, to stand by him.
We can't wait to be with him—
we're going to see the king!

Chorus…

## Meet the baby

**Verse 1**
Feel the splinters in your hand
as you push the wooden door
Hear the creaking rusty hinge
and the rustle of the straw
Smell the warmth of the animals
and the hint of spice in the air
See the silver starlight on the manger there.

**Chorus**
*Come into the stable*
*Come, one and all*
*Come and meet the baby king*
*So great and so small.*

**Verse 2**
Brush your hand against a wing
that's whiter than a bird.
Is there music playing here,
the sweetest that you've heard?
Catch a glimpse of a shimmering face
as another angel leans down
Breathe the scent of lilies
from the heavenly crowd.

**Chorus…**

**Verse 3**
Touch the furry donkey's head
as you tiptoe softly by
Hear the murmur of the crowd
and the sleepy newborn cry
Catch your breath in astonishment
and hold out your finger, because
You see the eyes of Jesus gazing into yours.

**Chorus…**

*Ariel pulls Loreal off. All on stage sing 'Meet the baby'.*

✣

*Ariel and Loreal enter and walk up to the baby on level 2. Loreal is holding his/her nose ostentatiously.*

**Loreal:**  I tell you, Ariel, I just can't stand…

*Loreal looks up, surprised, and lets go of his nose. He stops wobbling and stands up straight and smiles.*

**Ariel:**  What's the matter?
**Loreal:**  For the first time since I set foot on earth, it feels like heaven. It feels the right way up. It feels like this is how it ought to be. Why?
**Ariel:**  We're in the one stable place on earth. Look.

*They both kneel down by Mary holding Jesus.*

**Loreal:**  The baby!
**Ariel:**  God himself.
**Loreal:**  Come down to live on earth.
**Ariel:**  That's topsy turvy!
**Loreal:**  It's so upside down, it's the right way up!

**Ariel:** Amazing!

**Loreal:** Dear Jesus, forgive me for thinking
I was too important to come and help
the people in this topsy turvy world.
Help me to help you put things the
right way up.

*All umbrellas are now held the right way up.*

*Optional carol: On Christmas night all Christians sing*

*All sing 'Topsy turvy world'.*

## ✶✶✶✶✶✶✶✶✶✶✶✶✶✶✶✶✶✶✶✶✶✶✶✶✶✶✶✶✶✶

### Topsy turvy world

It's a topsy turvy world we live in
But God came at Christmas
from heaven above.
It's a topsy turvy world we live in
And lived, died, and rose up
to show us his love
This love shows the way we can
change things around
It's a topsy turvy world we live in
But working with God we can turn it
right way round.

✶✶✶✶✶✶✶✶✶✶✶✶✶✶✶✶✶✶✶✶✶✶✶✶✶✶✶✶✶✶

*All chant. On the words 'Christmas time', the actors on the outer edges raise up umbrellas in final tableau.*

## ✶✶✶✶✶✶✶✶✶✶✶✶✶✶✶✶✶✶✶✶✶✶✶✶✶✶✶✶✶✶

### Topsy turvy chant

Inside out and upside down
and all head-over-heels are turning
Back to front and round and round
and wheels in wheels in wheels are turning
Bottoms up and wrong side out
and willy-nilly vice versa
Crazy, madcap, Christmas crackers,
tables turned and hurdy-gurdy,
Topsy turvy Christmas time!

✶✶✶✶✶✶✶✶✶✶✶✶✶✶✶✶✶✶✶✶✶✶✶✶✶✶✶✶✶✶

*THE END*

Reproduced with permission from *Topsy Turvy Christmas* published by BRF 2003 (1 84101 340 4)

# THE SONGS

## TOPSY TURVY CHANT

Inside out and upside down and all head-over-heels are turning
Back to front and round and round and wheels in wheels in wheels are turning
Bottoms up and wrong side out and willy-nilly vice versa
Crazy, madcap, Christmas crackers, tables turned and hurdy-gurdy,
Topsy turvy Christmas time!

# TOPSY TURVY CHANT

Piano

Words & Music Lucy Moore
Arranged by Neil Ogley

# TOPSY TURVY WORLD

It's a topsy turvy world we live in
We long for peace but we end up with war
It's a topsy turvy world we live in
We have enough and we still long for more
And we fight and we kill for a few miles of ground
It's a topsy turvy world we live in
Find me a place where it all comes right way round.

It's a topsy turvy world we live in
Children go hungry and starve on the street
It's a topsy turvy world we live in
Others are dying from too much to eat
And there's plenty for all if we shared it around
It's a topsy turvy world we live in
Find me a time when it all comes right way round.

It's a topsy turvy world we live in
We fly into space but so many don't know
In this topsy turvy world we live in
About him who made us to live, love and grow
And we've found out so much, but there's one we've not found.
It's a topsy turvy world we live in
Find me the one who will bring the right way round.

**Reprise:**
It's a topsy turvy world we live in
But God came at Christmas from heaven above.
It's a topsy turvy world we live in
And lived, died, and rose up to show us his love
And this love shows the way we can change things around
It's a topsy turvy world we live in
But working with God we can turn it right way round.

Reproduced with permission from *Topsy Turvy Christmas* published by BRF 2003 (1 84101 340 4)

# TOPSY TURVY WORLD

Piano

Words & Music Lucy Moore
Arranged by Neil Ogley

# NAZARETH CALYPSO

There's an angel walkin' into town tonight
In our dirty streets he's a radiant light
And his wings brush the shabby houses, making them bright
Oh oh! This angel is a marvellous sight.
Oh yes! This angel is a marvellous sight.

There's a young girl singin' to her God tonight
A joyful song 'cos she's full of light.
She's about to get herself a terrible fright
Oh oh! About to see a marvellous sight.
Oh yes! About to see a marvellous sight.

There's a Spirit moving in the house tonight
Mary reckons it'll be all right.
Goes along with God without a fight
Oh oh! She wants to help him put things right.
Oh yes! She wants to help him put things right.

# NAZARETH CALYPSO

Piano

Words & Music Lucy Moore
Arranged by Neil Ogley

# HEAVEN'S JUST FOR US

Piano

Words & Music Lucy Moore
Arranged by Neil Ogley

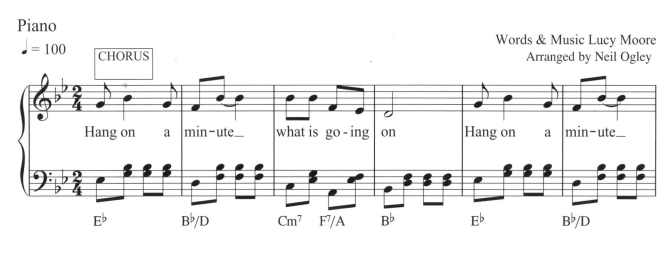

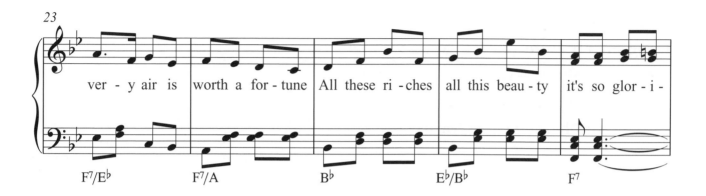

ver - y air is worth a for-tune All these ri - ches all this beau - ty it's so glor - i -

F7/Eb   F7/A   Bb   Eb/Bb   F7

ous But all of this be - longs in heaven and hea - ven's just for us

Bb   F7/A   Gm   F   Cm7   F7/A   Bb

# HEAVEN'S JUST FOR US

Hang on a minute—what is going on?
Hang on a minute—it's all going wrong!
Hang on a minute—we won't make a fuss
But all of this belongs in heaven
And heaven's just for us!

### Verse 1

Now God could take the wealth of heaven
And drop it on the earth.
These piles of gold, these precious jewels
This very air is worth a fortune.
All these riches, all this beauty—it's so glorious
But all of this belongs in heaven
And heaven's just for us!

### Verse 3

And God could take the joy of heaven
And wrap it round the world
Like a lovely rainbow ribbon
Every inch all curled and dancing.
All this laughter, all this fun—it's so obvious
That all of this belongs in heaven
And heaven's just for us!

**CHORUS...**

### Verse 2

And God could take the love of heaven
And pour it on the planet.
Love that changes lives around
That softens granite hearts and minds.
Oh, all this tender Father's love—
there's plenty of surplus
But all of this belongs in heaven
And heaven's just for us!

**CHORUS...**

**CHORUS...**

# JOSEPH'S SONG

### Verse 1

All I ever wanted was a peaceful life
The safety of my job and then a faithful wife
A stable happy home and a normal family
Now it seems the strangest things are happening to me.

### CHORUS:

Joseph, you had your life planned out
Joseph, in your quiet little town
Joseph, you'd ruled surprises out
But God's about to turn your plans upside down.

### Verse 2

All I ever wanted was a son to teach
About the wood and nails and the price of each
And all I asked from life was predictability
Now it seems the strangest things are happening to me.

### CHORUS...

### Verse 3

All you ever wanted was to do God's will
Deep inside your heart you know you want that still
Take Mary as your wife—the baby's God's, it's true
You will love the strange things that are happening to you.

### CHORUS...

# JOSEPH'S SONG

Piano

Words & Music Lucy Moore
Arranged by Neil Ogley

# MOVING ON BLUES

I've got those moving on blues.
(Da da da da da da da da da da)
'Cos I had to leave my home
(Da da da da da da da da da da)
Though there's holes in my shoes
(Da da da da da da da da da da)
Me and my donkey, got to roam.
(Da da da da da da da da da da)

Leaving all my folk behind
(Da da da da da da da da da da)
Face an unknown world ahead
(Da da da da da da da da da da)
There are times this world ain't kind
(Da da da da da da da da da da)
Wish I could stay at home in bed
(Da da da da da da da da da da)

Oh how slow the miles pass
(Da da da da da da da da da da)
When the traffic's all in queues
(Da da da da da da da da da da)
Now my donkey's out of gas
(Da da da da da da da da da da)
I really got those moving on blues.
(Da da da da da da da da da da)

Ah-ha.

# MOVING ON BLUES

Piano

Words & Music Lucy Moore
Arranged by Neil Ogley

# INNKEEPER'S SONG

We've plenty of room, come in, come in!
You're welcome, you're welcome to stay.
Our six-star hotel will ring out the bells
You're welcome, you're welcome today!

Roll out the red carpet and bow to the ground.
Let trumpeters fanfare—hooray!
You're our VIPs, oh, do sit down, please
You're welcome, you're welcome today!

We'll carry your luggage, we'll garage your ass.
Would you care for a small canapé?
You're special to us, you are worth all this fuss.
You're welcome, you're welcome today!

Oh, have some champagne! Take some more caviar!
Of course we'll expect you to pay
But relax for the mo, 'cos we're longing to show you
You're welcome, so welcome today!

# INNKEEPER'S SONG

Piano

Words & Music Lucy Moore
Arranged by Neil Ogley

We've plen-ty of room__ come in__ come in__ you're

wel - come you're wel - come to stay_____ Our six - star ho - tel__ will

ring out the bells You're wel - come you're wel - come to - day

# ANGELS' SONG

Words Lucy Moore
Music Paul Moore
Arranged by Neil Ogley

# ANGELS' SONG

**CHORUS *(X 2)*:**
From the highest of the high
To the lowest of the low
Let peace and love and blessings flow.

**Verse 1**
Higher than the highest thought
Higher than the starry sky
Higher price than any gift you've bought
He is God, the king on high.

**CHORUS...**

**Verse 2**
To the ones the world ignored
To the outcasts and the poor
To the ones who try to please the Lord
God's peace comes for evermore.

**CHORUS...**

**Verse 3**
So from the highest heights of glory
God has come to lowest earth.
Tell the world the Christmas story
Tell the world of Jesus' birth.

**CHORUS...**

# STAR SONG

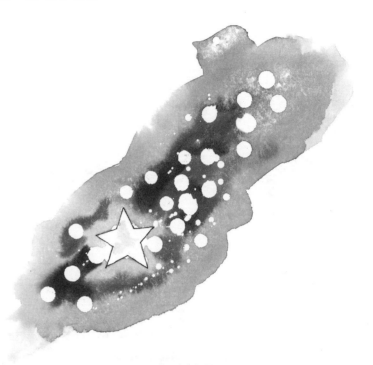

### Verse 1

Back a billion years ago
God made me to twinkle so
Pouring light out into space
Shining for a time and place
Where new worlds and hopes begin
Where they'll see the newborn king.

### CHORUS

Wisdom made me so bright
Shining out through the centuries
Wise scribes wrote of my meaning
While my rays of light were beaming
Wise men followed my light
If you're wise you'll follow me still.

### Verse 2

Back a thousand years ago
God wanted his friends to know
That his Son would come to them
And be born in Bethlehem
And they wrote in holy scrolls
Prophecies of what he told.

### CHORUS...

***(Sing Chorus and Verse 3 together,
unaccompanied)***

### Verse 3

So I shine with all my might
Knowing that tonight's the night
When the plans of countless years
Come to all their fullness here.
His amazing perfect plan:
God has come to earth as man.

# STAR SONG

# TREASURE SONG

You're after hidden treasure
You're after more than gold
The casket's rough and unrefined
But look inside and you will find
Riches untold.

You're searching for a treasure
Of far more worth than spice
Unlike the jar of frankincense
Its fragrance mystic and intense
This has no price.

You're hunting for a treasure
And there is only one
That's worth more than the myrrh you bring
Far greater than the greatest king
God's own Son.

# TREASURE SONG

Words & Music Lucy Moore
Arranged by Neil Ogley

Piano

♩. = 100

You're af - ter hid - den treas - ure You're aft - er more than gold_____ The cask - et's rough and un _ re - fined but look in - side and you will find rich - es un - told

Gm    Gm    E♭    Gm    D⁷    Gm    A/C♯    D/F♯    Gm    F⁷    Gm

♩ = 140

1. 2. & 3.

Last Time

Gm    D⁷    Gm

Reproduced with permission from *Topsy Turvy Christmas* published by BRF 2003 (1 84101 340 4)

# WE'RE GOING TO SEE THE KING!

**CHORUS**

We're so excited! *(Oh yes!)* We're going to see the king

Everyone's invited! *(Oh yes!)* We're all going in.

Don't care if we're rich or poor, doesn't matter any more

What matters is we're here for sure! *(Oh yes!)* We're going to see the king!


**Children**

We know it's past our bedtime, but we can't sleep a wink.

It feels more like playtime, and we'd all like to think

That we can be with Jesus any time of day or night

And so we've come to sit with him, to cuddle him, chill out with him

We can't wait to be with him—we're going to see the king!


**CHORUS...**


**Kings**

We know we're very tired after our three-year trip

We ought to go to bed now but we don't want to kip

We've come this far behind the star, and now I think we're here!

And so we've come to speak to him, to kneel to him, bow down to him

We can't wait to be with him—we're going to see the king!


**CHORUS...**

## Angels

We ought to be in paradise but can't resist the urge
To see him with our own two eyes, to fly right down to earth.
Our mighty God become a child? Amazing, but it's true!
And so we've come to honour him, to gaze on him and worship him.
We can't wait to be with him—we're going to see the king!

**CHORUS...**

## Shepherds / Farmer

We know we should be guarding our sheep out on the hill
But it would be too hard when we're so excited still.
We know we're only working-class, the lowest of the low
But we've come to smile at him, to sing to him, to play to him
We can't wait to be with him—we're going to see the king!

**CHORUS...**

## Animals

We know we're unhygienic and we make a nasty smell
But we make the place look scenic and we warm it up as well
We know we're only animals, but God's our Maker too
And so we've come to stare at him, to breathe on him, to stand by him.
We can't wait to be with him—we're going to see the king!

**CHORUS...**

 Reproduced with permission from *Topsy Turvy Christmas* published by BRF 2003 (1 84101 340 4)

# WE'RE GOING TO SEE THE KING!

Piano ♩ = 110

Words & Music Lucy Moore
Arranged by Neil Ogley

# MEET THE BABY

### Verse 1

Feel the splinters in your hand as you push the wooden door
Hear the creaking rusty hinge and the rustle of the straw
Smell the warmth of the animals and the hint of spice in the air
See the silver starlight on the manger there.

### CHORUS

Come into the stable
Come, one and all
Come and meet the baby king
So great and so small.

### Verse 2

Brush your hand against a wing that's whiter than a bird.
Is there music playing here, the sweetest that you've heard?
Catch a glimpse of a shimmering face as another angel leans down
Breathe the scent of lilies from the heavenly crowd.

### CHORUS...

### Verse 3

Touch the furry donkey's head as you tiptoe softly by
Hear the murmur of the crowd and the sleepy newborn cry
Catch your breath in astonishment and hold out your finger, because
You see the eyes of Jesus gazing into yours.

### CHORUS...

# TOPSY TURVY CHRISTMAS CD

### 13 original songs, plus traditional carols for Christmas

INCLUDES VOCAL & BACKING TRACKS FOR SONGS

1 84101 298 X, £8.99

The Topsy Turvy Christmas CD comprises vocal and backing tracks of all thirteen original songs from the musical play, plus musical arrangements for the traditional carols suggested in the play. The music can be used to accompany the play, or enjoyed on its own in school assemblies, end of year events and at home.
To order, visit your local Christian bookshop or the BRF website, www.brf.org.uk

| **Original songs from the play** | **Traditional carols** |
|---|---|
| 1. Topsy Turvy chant | 1. Angels from the realms of glory |
| 2. Topsy turvy world | 2. It came upon the midnight clear |
| 3. Nazareth calypso | 3. Thou who wast rich beyond all splendour |
| 4. Heaven's just for us | 4. In the bleak midwinter |
| 5. Joseph's song | 5. The first nowell |
| 6. Moving on blues | 6. While shepherds watched |
| 7. Innkeeper's song | 7. Hark the herald angels sing |
| 8. Shepherds' rap | 8. We three kings |
| 9. Angels' song | 9. Away in a manger |
| 10. Star song | 10. Silent night |
| 11. Treasure song | 11. See him lying on a bed of straw |
| 12. We're going to see the king | 12. O come all ye faithful |
| 13. Meet the baby | 13. On Christmas night all Christians sing |